Neuroscience and Critical Thinking

Understand the Hidden Pathways of Your Thought Patterns - Improve Your Memory, Make Rational Decisions, Tune Down Emotional Reactions, and Set Realistic Expectations

Written by
Albert Rutherford

Printed in the United States of America

Published by Kindle Direct Publishing

Email: albertrutherfordbooks@gmail.com

Table of Contents

Introduction

Thinking is something we do every day, often unconsciously. When you make your breakfast, brush your teeth, and drive to work, you're thinking. But have you ever thought about your thought processes, how you make decisions like what to eat for lunch and when to wake up to get to work?

Thinking about your thought process is known as *metacognition*. Having awareness of how your thoughts work is the first step toward developing critical thinking skills. Critical thinking is a method you can use to examine your thoughts and beliefs carefully, and be able to thoughtfully engage with other people's ideas. This will make your everyday conversations and decisions easier and more carefully considered, but it can also help you solve bigger issues. The best thinkers in the world use critical thinking strategies to help solve major problems like getting to Mars, global climate change, and nuclear disarmament. These sound too large to tackle on your own, but if you think about the questions behind them, they suddenly become much more solvable. What is the cause of climate change? Who is responsible for this cause? How do you get them to change their practices? What would this process look like? What makes it effective? Starting to think about these things is how even the most brilliant people do their work.

You can apply this to smaller scale problems, too: If you want to start exercising, how do you know what to do? Which workout program is right for you? To solve this problem, you can break it down: Do you want to get stronger or be able to run faster? What health benefits are you looking for? Is one workout as good for you as it claims to be? How would you figure out the quality of the exercise you're looking at? Luckily, we have access to more information through the Internet than ever before, but the problem with this information is that it's not always accurate or valuable to the problem you want to solve. Critical thinking skills will help you sift through this information and use it to its full potential.

The brain is an amazing organ. Not only can it think, it can also think about how it thinks. It can think about the past, imagine the future, and imagine things that never happened. But the brain can also trick us. We all have biases that we are unaware of, based on our experiences and knowledge, which influence how we think and can cloud our judgment. Humans evolved emotions as tools for survival, but they can also work against our reasoning. Emotions and "gut instincts" tend to guide us to conclusions that are not always correct. Instead, they tend to be the conclusions that are easiest, that we feel the most comfortable with based on our biases, because this was a good survival strategy for early humans. They lived in a world where it was useful to have these instincts, but the modern world is much more complicated. It is more important than ever to carefully examine our perspectives and thought processes, for the good of ourselves and all of humanity.

You can think of critical thinking as a set of strategies to help guide us away from emotional, biased decision-making and toward rational consideration of our actions and beliefs. This helps us become independent thinkers who can make our own choices thoughtfully. The skills one develops as a critical thinker include understanding the logic that underlies ideas and theories, being able to deconstruct and formulate arguments, finding the holes and flaws in arguments, being able to construct step-by-step solutions, determining the validity of ideas, and being able to examine the reasoning behind your own beliefs. You might notice that critical thinking doesn't just mean knowing facts. It is an entirely different process than memorization or absorbing information; being good at remembering things doesn't make you a good critical thinker! Critical thinkers focus more on *how* they know than *what* they know. This means they're able to *use* what they know to predict the consequences of actions, solve problems, and determine what information to use when they want to learn something new.[i]

Critical thinking doesn't mean "being critical," either. In fact, a big part of critical thinking is being able to hold a well-reasoned, calm, intellectual debate. Critical thinking will allow you to deconstruct people's arguments and show them why they're wrong, without resorting to personal insults or petty words. This will actually make it easier to work with people you don't agree with. Critical thinking is a great strategy to use in group projects and collaborative work, precisely because it creates ideal conditions for intellectual interaction.

This intellectual process doesn't necessarily need to stunt creativity. Although we often think of logic as being diametrically opposed to creativity, the whole idea behind critical thinking is that you can use logical guideposts to stimulate your creativity. Logical examination of every idea means that you could actually find that a less-popular idea is the most sound one, or that there is a better solution than the ones you've previously thought of for the problems you're considering. Using critical thinking skills can open up entire worlds that you've never even considered before.

We are not born with critical thinking skills. Instead, we have to learn them and practice them to be able to use them well. The good news is that anyone can learn how to think critically! Like any process of self-improvement, learning critical thinking begins with recognizing the things you need to improve. This means realizing what the errors are in our own thinking.

There are several different types of these errors. The first you have to think about are logical fallacies, or the errors you're making in the logic of your thought process. You also have to consider your prior assumptions and which ones are false; this can be one of the most difficult things to realize, but some of the things you've always "known" aren't necessarily right. You also should question your memory (which is not always accurate) and whether your guesses and "gut feelings" are right. All these errors will be discussed in more detail in later chapters, but for now they're definitely something to consider.

Fortunately, we can compensate for these common thinking errors. This is where metacognition becomes very important—for example, you have to think about how you came to remember something in order to assess whether it really happened. You can use processes like keeping track of your progress in your thinking by journaling, implementing changes if you notice something isn't working or moving forward, being intentional in your thinking strategies, and thinking about how what you've learned connects to what you know. You can think about this process of metacognition as adopting scientific skepticism about what you've never previously questioned. "Scientific skepticism" means doubting *intelligently*, examining your thinking process and how you know what you know using objective evidence. Examining your thoughts like they're a scientific subject will help you find what science always works toward: the truth, rather than what we want to be the truth.[ii]

"Wishful thinking" can be especially harmful to our critical thinking because it guides us to the conclusions we want instead of the correct ones. The best way to counteract this is to focus on the objective evidence you collect, instead of conjecture or prior knowledge. For example, if you're feeling nauseous and have a headache all the time, you could Google your symptoms or ask your friends, or go to a doctor. Which seems like it would provide the best answer to your problem? Clearly, a doctor with years of medical training will be better able to assess your symptoms with objective evidence and provide you with a reliable conclusion than a Wiki page or your friend. Therefore, they will actually tell you what is wrong (if anything) and prevent you from jumping to the conclusion that you have a serious illness.

Of course, your doctor represents real science—an important aspect of this source of information, because there is pseudoscience that will also lead you to incorrect conclusions. For example, if you decide to go to a crystal healer, they will be less likely to successfully heal your symptoms than your doctor. This is because their training is not based on objective, rigorously reviewed evidence. You can always tell whether something is real science by the methodology it follows. It doesn't follow a set of unsubstantiated beliefs. Instead, it follows a very specific, well-reasoned, logical path of assessment to reach a conclusion. A critical thinker can recognize this, and make choices about what to believe based on this recognition.

The next important thing that a critical thinker understands is the nature of knowledge. The only scientifically observable evidence is natural; the natural phenomena we see every day therefore must have natural causes. Supernatural causes have not been proven observable with scientific methods (despite what ghost hunters might have you believe) because they are not empirically measurable. Critical thinkers know that even scientific theories are not the same as facts; there is always a chance for human error when making empirical observations. This means that information can always be improved upon with new data—and this is a good thing! As long as empirical evidence is used to reach our conclusions and knowledge, it is more carefully considered than a belief reached without critical thinking.

If we don't rely on critical thinking, we can fall prey to delusional thinking, where we completely live in our own reality or one constructed by others. These realities cannot be true, because they're not based on empirical observations. If we rely on our emotions and non-evidential beliefs, we move further and further away from the facts of the issue because our views warp them. This is known as confirmation bias; we become more interested in finding evidence that supports our views instead of deriving conclusions from the evidence we see. In an era where we have access to more information and misinformation than ever, it is vital to use critical thinking to avoid being manipulated into incorrect beliefs, whether with respect to wellness, politics, or consumer goods. Applying thinking strategies will help you navigate this sea of information to find the facts.

You might already know some strong critical thinkers! They tend to share the following traits:

- Curiosity about a wide variety of subjects;

- Being aware of situations where they can use critical thinking;

- Confidence in their own reasoning;

- Commitment to being well-informed;

- Understanding others' opinions;

- Openness to revising beliefs;

- Objectivity in assessing reasoning;

- Self-awareness of own biases and thinking flaws;

- Careful judgment when changing opinions; and

- Changing when an argument is well-reasoned enough

As you can tell, the key to becoming a good critical thinker is self-awareness. You need to be able to honestly assess the things you previously thought were true, as well as the thought processes that led you to those conclusions. If you weren't using good logic, or if your thought process was influenced by your experiences and emotions, then reconsider using critical thinking! Realize that people, by nature, are very good at coming up with explanations for thought processes that were flawed. A dead giveaway for these sorts of incorrect conclusions is that your beliefs contradict each other. If they do, this means your conclusions might have been a result of confirmation bias, but if you know this, you can get closer to the truth!

Critical thinkers also know that they need to ask other people about their own ideas and beliefs. Critical thinking cannot happen in a vacuum. Other people can offer perspectives that you have never even considered, and they can find holes in your logic that you missed completely. You don't need to focus on agreeing with others, because this could also lead to issues with bias, but a critical discussion is an extremely helpful intellectual exercise. Approaching others can also help you realize that the scope of your own knowledge is not infinite. No one person can know everything. But by sharing and critically evaluating knowledge, we can expand it. It's okay if this makes you uncomfortable. In fact, getting out of your comfort zone is important to expanding your beliefs and your thinking. Critical thinking is not about knowing things, and certainly not about affirming what you already know. Instead, it is about finding the truth—and making that what you know.

Chapter 1: The Neuroscience of Belief and Perception

Let's say you want to get a dog, and although you're open to any breed, there's one breed that you're really interested in. Let's say the breed you're partial to is corgis. You stop by your local shelter and there are several dogs you like, one of which is a corgi. Obviously you have to do your research on these different dogs. What do you choose to type into Google? You might search for "pit bull dangerous" or "Jack Russell energetic," while for the breed you favor you don't ask those questions. Instead, you type in things like "corgis good with kids" or "corgis easy to train." Obviously, these different questions will give you different answers. Although the Jack Russell or the pit bull you saw in the shelter might actually make a great dog for you—pit bulls being dangerous is a myth, and Jack Russell terriers can still make good family dogs—your results will confirm with positive results the choice you were already partial to: the corgi. You did your research, but your brain was selecting information based on the unconscious bias you already had. You fell prey to an all-too-human problem: we believe what we want to believe.

This isn't a conscious choice. Our brains are neurologically wired to base our beliefs on what we want to believe, because these are emotional responses. Emotional responses were useful to people when we had to run away from animals that wanted to eat us, but they can cloud rational thought processes in the modern world. However, if we understand this, we can also work to mitigate the effects of our emotional biases on our brains.

Our brains operate on three levels: the "human brain," the "primate brain," and the "reptilian brain." This is known as the "triune brain model" and was developed by the neuroscientist Paul MacLean. According to the model, these three "brains" correspond to physical parts of our brain (the neocortex, the limbic system, and the basal ganglia), and the level at which they operate corresponds to when we evolved them. The "human brain," or the neocortex, being the newest part of our brain in terms of evolution, can be controlled by the older parts. A lot of our cognitive processes, including emotions, actually occur subconsciously in these older parts. They were developed early in evolution because they help us make quick decisions, which was important to our survival when we hadn't yet developed more complex thinking. For example, if you smell pungent chemicals, your revulsion tells you not to eat them; this keeps you alive, and is quicker and more effective than reasoning out why you shouldn't consume the thing you smell.[iii]

The reptilian brain is the oldest of our three brains. It is controlled by the basal ganglia, which are at the center of the human brain and are found in every animal, including reptiles and birds. Theorists think that the brains of reptiles and other early-evolution-stage animals were largely made of this brain-area. Therefore, the theory goes that the basal ganglia were developed first. The basal ganglia control self-preservation behaviors that are necessary to an animal's survival. These behaviors include feeding ourselves, fighting threats, fleeing danger that can't be fought, and reproductive behaviors. Implied in these behaviors are other fundamental actions such as self-defense, defense of family, communication, social cues, and protecting territory or property. MacLean calls these behaviors "species-typical" ones.

Although the reptilian brain is clearly very useful in the wild, it still has advantages in the modern world. Every time we encounter danger, the "fight-flight-freeze" response we experience is controlled by the reptilian brain. It also helps us detect danger before it even happens; this is how people can "sense" a home invasion, a robbery, or even an encounter with a dangerous character before it even happens. On a more basic level, this part of our brain has a visceral reaction to the familiar versus the unfamiliar. This is why an unfamiliar situation causes excitement and gets your heart racing, even if it's a fun adventure and not dangerous! The reptilian brain relaxes around the familiar, while it gives us adrenaline and an automatic suspicious reaction when we're around the unfamiliar. This reaction is behind such powerful reactions as nostalgia and homesickness. Advertisers often capitalize on these emotions, and try to remind us of familiar things to form a connection and make us feel safe with a product.[iv]

Understanding the reptilian brain is important, because it's where the "gut instincts" people often talk about come from. Although these instincts help us survive in dangerous situations, they can also mislead us when we know we're safe but still in an unfamiliar situation. For example, if you're in a different country and a different culture, and you can't speak the language, your reptilian brain might prompt you towards being fearful even though you don't need to be. It can also make you reject unfamiliar ideas simply because they are new to you. The reptilian brain is at the root of our successful evolution, but it's also at the root of many of humanity's ugliest impulses. That is why it is so important for us to understand this aspect of our neurological makeup.

The reptilian brain's activity is also related to the living conditions in which we find ourselves. You might have heard of Maslow's hierarchy of needs. This theory was developed by

Abraham Maslow and describes what our emotional needs are based on our situations in life. We have basic needs like food and shelter but people also need to feel safe and loved. Eventually, if all your other emotional needs are met, you can develop self-esteem and finally something called self-actualization. Self-actualization is the state where we are our best selves, where we are free to explore our potential because we have no other needs to fulfill. Our neurological structures somewhat mirror this hierarchy, because the parts of our brain that require basic needs are able to drown out the parts that govern the "lesser needs." The neocortex, in addition to being the most "recent" part of our brain, also governs self-actualization. Maslow's hierarchy is not static; you can be at several different levels of needs (for example, you can have hunger and still love and be loved). It's just meant to reflect what is happening in our brains when we need certain things.[v]

Our brains are wired to avoid punishment and prize rewards. This evolved so that we would learn to emotionally avoid things that harm us; we feel bad after punishment, while our brains receive more dopamine when we get rewards. Dopamine is a chemical that causes us to feel good; developing a tolerance to it can also lead to problems like addiction. This evolutionary reaction motivates our thought process to avoid punishment and pursue reward, even though this might not be the correct decision.[vi]

Human needs have other effects on our thought processes. We feel a deep psychological need for control over our own actions and lives, which can manifest itself in common flaws in critical thinking. Superstitions are born out of this need for control, because it creates the illusion that we have control over things that are out of our power. Wearing your favorite jersey or wearing a crystal won't actually help your team win or bring you a better day, but they make you think you have some control over these things. Superstitions also give our arbitrary world a sense of meaning and purpose in the context of our lives. This also plays into the deep human needs for connection and meaning in life, which also release dopamine into our brains when we believe they are there. To chase this feeling, we often engage in thought processes that are clearly marred by confirmation bias and wishful thinking.

Humans also crave simple explanations for complex issues because this makes problems less overwhelming and more controllable. Although simplification might make our problems seem easier to solve, it actually impedes us from reaching critically assessed solutions. It is important to recognize and break down all the complexities of a problem when using critical thinking. At its worst, oversimplification of differences leads to bigotry against others. The reality of our lives is always more complicated than our brains want us to believe.

As a species, we feel a deep psychological need for meaning in our lives. This gives us a purpose, a reason to survive, reproduce, and propagate the species. Although this is clearly beneficial from an evolutionary standpoint, it can again lead to confirmation bias in our thinking. We say that "things happen for a reason," and we try to apply logic to random events even when they weren't under human control. Conspiracy theories are an example of this; people concoct illogical explanations for traumatic events like assassinations and terrorist attacks because they cannot handle the idea of such a terrible event being random. They cling to them even if they make no sense logically.

We also need to feel respected by our community, and to feel good about ourselves. We developed this out of an evolutionary need to belong to a group and to be protected. However, this can also introduce critical thinking errors. People often search for external reasons for why they mess up instead of blaming themselves, or persuade themselves that they couldn't help the mistake they made. These defense mechanisms protect us from embarrassment or shame, but they also cloud our ability to clearly evaluate and learn from our mistakes. Our instinct to please people also means that we try to avoid making them angry or sad, and we can convince ourselves to hold opinions that aren't well-reasoned.

Another common logical foible is cognitive dissonance, or when we hold two different opinions at once. It can be difficult for us to recognize this because of our tendency to reinforce our self-esteem, but this is one of the most important roadblocks to developing critical thinking skills. If you become aware that two of your beliefs conflict, this is a sign that you should examine your knowledge to see what you need to investigate. To do this, however, you need to be especially careful to not rationalize away the mistakes you made in acquiring these beliefs. Human nature is a big obstacle to rational thought!

Think about your morals. Believe it or not, this is an evolved part of our brain, too! We, and other members of the animal kingdom, need a moral code so our social groups can function. Could you buy a house that a murderer had owned? Probably not, right? There's no rational, critically reasoned explanation as to why you wouldn't do it—most people would cite bad karma or ghosts—but you'd still think it's contaminated somehow. We've evolved this response for a reason. Of course you wouldn't want to bring yourself close to a murderer, you've evolved to avoid anything that could kill you!

Using critical thinking in your everyday life can be more of an uphill battle than many people think. I probably couldn't successfully get you to change your mind on the murder house with rational arguments. Changing old superstitions, beliefs, and habits is hard! However, peer pressure can help. We tend to adapt the behaviors of the people around us because of our drive to be part of a community. Surrounding yourself with other critical thinkers, therefore, will help you emulate their habits!

When we think of "intelligence," we often think of someone's intellectual skills or their body of knowledge. However, as we know, this does not make you a perfect decision-maker or critical thinker. There is another type of intelligence called "emotional intelligence." This is where you're aware of your emotions, know what they are, and are able to control them enough that you can actually use them to help you solve problems.

This means that you can healthily process your own emotions and understand and empathize with other people. To date, psychologists have not come up with a system for rating emotional intelligence the way they have for general intelligence. This means that many experts are skeptical, but it is a popular concept in the business world, where some employers have decided to administer "tests" in the hope of finding better employees. It is important to note that there is no established link between workplace success and emotional intelligence. Regardless, it might make up for the lack of correlation between general intelligence and decision-making skills.

Think of the optical illusion artworks you've seen online or in art classes. How is your brain fooled into thinking something in a 3-D movie is actually coming towards you, or that a picture of a spiral is moving when it's not? The answer is that the brain can only process so much incoming information. Optical illusions take advantage of the quirks in our brain's processing to give us information that contradicts reality. Magicians and mentalists exploit the same aspect of our brain structure; they can fool us because they know what parts of a trick to show our brains. Our brains can also create an entirely new perception that isn't included in the data our brains receive. For example, in the phenomenon known as the McGurk effect, when audio of one sound is played over the lip movements of someone making another sound, we actually experience a third sound, especially when the audio quality is bad. This is due to our brain's attempt to synthesize conflicting information from our senses.[vii]

All these phenomena are examples of how sensory information can be deceptive. Our brains filter and interpret all the data our senses provide, in ways that are not necessarily accurate. Just think about how many times a day you mishear people! Your eyes can also be fooled; in a study known as the "invisible gorilla" test, researchers found that when people were asked to focus on people bouncing basketballs in a video, they totally missed that a person in a gorilla suit was walking in and out of the frame. Even when they were told about the gorilla and said that they wouldn't miss it, they generally did! This shows that when we focus hard on one piece of information, we miss a lot of other information. This skews our perception of reality. What we see or hear is not necessarily what is actually happening!

We like to think that we are good multitaskers, especially in today's demanding workplace. However, studies have shown that no one is a good multitasker—it's not in our nature! Instead, we simply direct our focus from one thing to another. Our brain's focused nature means that we often don't notice the changes happening around us, like a light turning on and off, or a squirrel moving around a tree. These things are part of reality, we're just unable to see them! Our perceptions are influenced by the way our brains process information, and we have to be aware of that as critical thinkers. Seeing is not believing, and this is why critical thinking skills are so important.

Chapter 2: Memory and Error

Think of your earliest memory. Is it of you running around at the playground, going to an amusement park, or meeting your sibling? Can you picture what was happening?

Chances are, this memory was actually completely invented by your brain. We don't have a video recorder attached to our eyes. Our brain is responsible for constructing our memories, and therefore our memories are not necessarily a reflection of reality. Instead, they are influenced by our preexisting beliefs and biases, which shape them into the reality that our brains accept. Before we start diving into critical thinking, we have to explore the nature of memory in detail so we can understand how our brains construct what we remember and know.

The part of our memory that we use the most in everyday life is our short-term memory. This is information that we've recently processed, and that we can remember without much conscious effort. This act of remembering is temporary. We often forget what is stored in the short-term memory in the long term. Research shows that we can only remember about seven things using short-term memory, and we can only access it up to a minute after we've processed the information. This might seem like barely using your memory, but it's actually very important. For example, when someone talks to you, you need to remember the previous words they've said to understand their statement. Short-term memory is also responsible for why we forget where we've put things; if our brains are thinking about too many other things, the location of the lost item gets bumped out of short-term memory. Our short-term memory evolved to be so small because it helps us focus on important things, like whether a lion is about to eat us, instead of being distracted by the stick we recently stepped on. Short-term memory, like bias and emotions, is designed to help us survive in the wild.[viii]

Since short-term memory occupies such a small space in our brains, we also don't hold complete memories there the way we keep long-term memories. Instead, our brains use signifiers like words and images that it can extrapolate from. Since this form of memory is so limited and fleeting, we have to make an effort to retain any information we want to remember in the long term. This effort can be in the form of repeating information, or breaking it down into smaller, simpler parts. You can also undertake a process of association like a "mind palace." Mind palaces are a mnemonic device where you have a mental picture of a house, and you put things you want to remember in different rooms so you build associations with certain images and other memories. Your motivation to remember something can also help you remember it—if you're on an amazing vacation and you say to yourself, "I want to remember this," you probably will!

Once you've completed this process of concentration, the piece of information you focused on will move to your long-term memory, which you keep over a longer period of time than you might think. Although you might think you don't remember much from childhood, you definitely remember your high school graduation clearly (even if it's been thirty years). In fact, there's a lot of debate over whether you actually forget memories, or if it just becomes more difficult over time to find them in your brain. Long-term memory primarily associates memories with meaning and other memories, which is why mnemonic device work. However, there is also evidence that our brain associates them with sound, which is probably why it's easier to remember song lyrics than book passages or poems.[ix]

How does this process of putting things in our long-term memory work in terms of the brain's physical structure? To process information for long-term memory, the brain actually rewires the structure of its neurons, or nerve cells. This is called long-term potentiation. Whenever we learn anything, it changes the way our brain's cells are organized, and can even create new brain cells! The structures formed by our neurons are called neural networks because neurons communicate with each other through them. When we develop new networks through learning, our neurons create proteins that help transfer neurotransmitters, or chemical signals that help brain cells communicate, through connections between the cells called synapses. Each time we use this connection, it gets stronger. These connections also bridge other parts of the brain, like the visual and auditory cortices, which helps us tie sensory data to our memories.

Short-term memory's physiology is temporary; it's mostly quick, temporary communications between the sensory part of our brain and the frontal, prefrontal, and parietal lobes (which mainly control fast decision-making). However, long-term memory is reflected in much more permanent, well-developed connections in our brains, which also end up covering a larger surface area. You might know the hippocampus as the part of our brain associated with memory, but it's not where long-term memories are stored. Instead, it helps transfer data from the short-term memory to the long-term, as well as jumpstarting the structural changes we've talked about.

So how does forgetting work? When we forget something, it means that the connections we formed in our neural networks have gotten weaker. Forgetting can also occur when our brains build a new network over the old one. Think of how, back in the day, you could tape over a video on VHS to store a different video; this latter way of forgetting is the same sort of process. This is why we often become forgetful when we feel burned out or overloaded with work. Our brains often "tape over" what was there before to store something new!

Have you ever wondered how much you have the potential to remember? In 2007, Richard Wiseman conducted an experiment called "Total Recall" to test exactly that—how much humans have the ability to remember. He did this by showing two volunteers (both female) 10000 images in two days, then testing them to see how many of the images they could remember. This type of experiment was not new; Lionel Standing first conducted this memory test in the early 1970s in Canada, where he found that his subjects could remember 70% of the images—or 7000 of the things they'd seen for only seconds at a time over just a couple of days! The problem with this study was that it was hard to replicate. Wiseman was the first to try.

Wiseman found that the subjects were, on average, better able to remember images if there were fewer of them, but he still found an amazing remembrance rate—on average, 98 percent for 612 images and 65 percent for 10,000 images. Neither test subject expected to remember so much. It turns out, we remember much more of what we see in our daily lives than we think, whether they're advertisements, faces, or traffic patterns. People actually have a very powerful visual memory.[x]

However, our memories are not like the easily accessible hard drive of a computer; they still have limits. The most obvious limit you might think of is when you can no longer remember something. This is often the only memory flaw we can readily detect, but it is not the only one. Our memories can also merge over time into a single memory, or they can change. This means that our memories are not always reliable, but interestingly enough, strong emotions can make for stronger memories.

Flashbulb memories are memories we have of sudden, unexpected things that are tied to strong emotions, instead of more everyday events. These tend to last longer than more quotidian memories and preserve more detail of the actual event. For example, most people who were alive during John F. Kennedy's assassination or 9/11 vividly remember where they were, what they were doing, and who they were with when they learned of the event because they felt strong emotions. This type of memory is often tied to emotional traumas, which is why sexual assault survivors also vividly remember attacks even if they happened long ago.

Roger Brown and James Kulik coined the term "flashbulb memory" in 1977 for traumatically charged memories. Their theory was that the brain captures these events so accurately because they are too difficult to process in the moment, and must be analyzed later when the person has more distance from the event. This provides the evolutionary advantage of learning from traumatic experiences to prevent them from recurring. [xi]

However, these memories do seem to degrade a little over time. A 1992 study by Ulric Neisser and Nicole Harsch assessed the nature of flashbulb memories. They asked 106 students about their memory of the *Challenger* explosion through a questionnaire. Two and a half years later, they gave the same group the same questionnaire. They then compared these questionnaires to assess how accurate the students' memories were two and a half years after the first survey. They found that a quarter of the students got a score of 0 on an accuracy scale of 0-7, and that 50 percent scored a 2 or below. This means that these students' memories of the event had degraded over a relatively short period of time. The students did recall the event—they just recalled it incorrectly. Their memories had altered over time.[xii]

After 9/11, a similar experiment was conducted. This time, participants' memories of mundane events were assessed in addition to their flashbulb memory of the traumatic event. These researchers found that the key difference between flashbulb memory and everyday memory was that patients had much more confidence in their flashbulb memories than in their ordinary memories. This confidence did not mean that the flashbulb memories were accurate. Confidence can make for vivid memories, but it does not necessarily mean they reflect reality.

Think of a fact that you're confident you know. Say you *know* that your Aunt Carol lived in Michigan a few years ago. But can you remember how you learned it? People often have trouble remembering where they learned something they're confident they remember. This is called "source amnesia." Source amnesia happens when your explicit memory, or the memory that you use to remember things like your anniversary or the time of an afternoon meeting, malfunctions. This is the counterpart of implicit memory, where we store subconscious things like knowing how to swim. Explicit memory is for things we intentionally memorize and remember, which makes it crucial for remembering our informational sources.[xiii]

Everyone experiences source amnesia, and for the most part, it won't hurt you. It's more important from an evolutionary perspective to remember what we know, instead of how we came to learn it; after all, knowing that "fire burns" is more important than remembering which person guided us away from it as a child. However, nowadays it is important to be able to cite our sources for information. Otherwise, we could end up believing lies or misinformation, or even end up spreading it ourselves, because we don't know if the source is reliable.

Humans also experience truth amnesia, which is the phenomenon where we remember a statement more than whether or not it is true. We tend to say "Oh, I've heard that before," without recognizing that we also heard that the statement was untrue. This is how rumors spread. If we're familiar with something, we remember the statement itself more than we remember its truthfulness, but the fact that we remember it makes us think it's true. Thus we can be convinced into assigning incorrect truthfulness to information we're actually merely acquainted with.[xiv] This is known as the "illusory truth effect," and was discovered in 1977 in a joint study undertaken by a team of researchers from Temple University and Villanova University. For example, we can think "Oh, I've heard something about Cuba being involved in JFK's assassination," but not remember that this has been debunked. We then have the overall impression that Cuba *was* involved in the assassination. This is what makes misinformation and "alternative facts" so insidious: If we don't make an effort to remember they're not true, our brains trick us into thinking they are. The power of suggestion is very powerful; repetition and reinforcement can convince us something is true. Hindsight bias is another form of this effect; if someone tells us something is true, we retroactively connect the dots to make ourselves believe we could have made that conclusion. Familiarity can be stronger than rational thought, so we have to watch out for it in critical thinking errors.[xv]

The final aspect of our memories that is important to understand in the context of critical thinking is that we have two different types: emotional memory and detail memory. Emotional memory is our general impression of what happened, and is, as you might have guessed, mostly tied to our emotions. For example, you can probably remember a time you were scared just from this suggestion of it. You probably have places or situations you associate with emotions like fear, even though you might not remember what the original event that makes you feel this way was. Meanwhile, your detail memory is related to exactly what it sounds like: details. Functional MRI scans taken when people recall these different types of memories have shown that they have different brain patterns, which means they stimulate different areas' neurological activity. This means that different parts of our brain handle details and broader emotions.[xvi]

Details are harder for us to remember, because in addition to having a much stronger neurological memory for emotions, our minds like to focus on the most compelling stimuli and tune out the rest. This is known as "selective attention," and it's actually a good thing because it prevents our brains from being overloaded with sensory data. Instead, we only remember the important details. For example, if you're attacked with a weapon, you definitely remember what the weapon was, but not necessarily the brand of the attacker's t-shirt.

The flip side of our tendency to block out small details is that our brain often fills these in for us in our memory—and it doesn't do this very well. These details are often altered or just plain incorrect. Most of the details you remember from any given situation are therefore actually constructed, rather than a direct recollection of what happened. These details can also change based on your broader knowledge base, because each time you learn new information your brain also updates the other things it knows. Our brains like to have a narrative of our experiences in the world, so it often changes our memories to fit that narrative. This is why we're so prone to exaggeration—our minds like to make us think dangers were bigger than they really were (of course, you can see how this would be helpful from an evolutionary perspective). The details in our memories are biased, constructed, and invented by necessity, and it's important that we recognize this. Researchers call this "memory contamination."

Think about a conversation you recently had with friends. If you ask your friends about it, their memories of what they said will likely be very different than yours, and the same will be true of your memories of your own words. This is because our brains are always biased toward our own narrative, and construct our memories to conform to that narrative. This is why it's important to share perspectives and recognize that people have contaminated memory by nature. We all have something important to contribute when reflecting on the past!

If you have a job where memory is important, this is especially important for you to keep in mind. Your memories, although you might have high confidence in them, are not always accurate. If you're a police officer who's interviewing witnesses about an incident, keep in mind that the witness's memory of that incident will be biased toward their own narrative. If you're a therapist, you need to keep in mind that your clients' memories are not always accurate, and might be influenced by psychological issues or a traumatic history. An important way to counter this is to ask open-ended questions that require more than yes or no answers, because they will produce more accurate results than a "leading" question like "Did you see the thief turn left at the intersection?" Coincidentally, this is why "open" questions are typically used in direct examination in court, where the lawyer is questioning their side's witness, and "leading" questions are used in cross-examination, where the lawyer is trying to poke holes in the other side's witness's testimony.

The FBI views "leading" questions as actually contaminating the interrogation process, and discourages its agents from using them. It also discourages the use of "coaching," which is the practice of leading a witness to give information that confirms the agent's hypothesis. This will lead to confirmation bias in the interrogation. For example, if the agent asks an interrogation subject about a specific suspect's presence at the scene of the crime, they are coaching them toward evidence against that suspect. Open-ended questions allow more room for the witness to give their own account of what they know.

Stress is also a big factor in memory, and FBI agents (as well as other law enforcement professionals) are encouraged to keep this in mind. A more relaxed person is more likely to give an accurate statement, rather than one geared towards what they think an interrogator wants to hear. Therefore, the FBI actively encourages "compassionate" procedures that keep in mind a subject's own narrative—that is, their culture, their biases, and their experiences. As you might have seen in criminal justice shows and podcasts like *Making a Murderer* and *Serial*, memory is one of the most useful tools available to law enforcement, but its fickleness means that witnesses need to be treated carefully. Otherwise, the justice system can fail to do its job and bring the right person to justice. [xvii]

It is important to recognize that while our memories are a valuable resource, they are rarely a 100-percent accurate account of reality. Our brains have evolved to create, twist, and construct our memories around our preexisting biases and personal narratives. The physical structures of our brain actually change along with our memories, which means that changes are often permanent until another change happens. We often fill in the gaps in the information we take in with details that are complete constructions, or even taken from a different memory (think of people's tendency to embellish their memories with details from movies they've seen). We often don't even know that we're doing this. To us, all our memories are true, and it can be difficult to impossible to spot a false memory. This means that critical thinking is an especially important tool when it comes to thinking about the past—that is, the process of creating history. [xviii]

Our memories are not reliable! If you can recognize this, you can work with others to construct an accurate picture of past events. This is what historians do every day, but you can even do this in your own life. Consider that conflicts might have actually been due to something you said or did, even though you don't remember it that way. Unless something is taped, written down, or collected in another objective manner, we can't trust that it was what really happened. Recognizing this is a crucial step to developing critical thinking skills. Memory is one resource, but evidence and logical reasoning are essential to discovering the truth.

Chapter 3: On Reality

Like memory and perception, reality is also something built in the brain. The brain works hard to create a reality that we can make sense of, but this reality is actually an illusion. Our brains build our reality from incoming data, but this involves a lot of filtering of information. This filtering process constructs a lot of the way we perceive the world. For example, this is why we feel like we have one collective consciousness, when really, disparate parts of our brain work together and converse to conduct our thought processes. Each part of your brain comes into conflict with the other parts as information moves through them, because they all serve different purposes. This conflict helps shape our reactions, and can lead to us making less-than-optimal choices.

Our neocortex does much of the labor involved in this "construction." This part of our brain controls our behaviors, planning, and decision-making on a more intellectual level than the other, more primitive parts of our brains that have already been discussed. However, the problem with the neocortex is that it applies these more sophisticated functions to things our primitive brains have already decided.

As an example, let's say you decided to replace your sibling's toothpaste with foot cream because you were angry at them. Your primitive brain motivated you to get revenge on them. Your neocortex might have originally thought, "This is wrong," which would obviously come into conflict with your more primitive impulses. If your neocortex wins, you'll decide not to go through with your plan because you've decided it's more rational not to. If your primitive brain wins, however, your neocortex will likely end up justifying your revenge for you with thought processes along the line of "They deserved it!" or "It's not that bad!" Once your brain decides which path to take, it gives your neurotransmitters dopamine to make you feel good about the fact that you've decided.

Although your decisions seem to be conscious and rational, they're not. Instead, we make our decisions subconsciously through an evolved process in our brains. In 2008, a team of researchers found that our brains exhibit neurological decision-making signals as much as ten seconds before we realize that we've made a decision. They conducted their experiment using fMRI scanning of patients who were assigned a task that forced them to make a decision between pressing two buttons, each representing a letter shown to subjects on a screen. The researchers found that in 60 percent of their trials, they were able to predict the subject's decision based on the location of their brain activity. The decision-making signal came from the frontopolar cortex, which is located right behind the forehead. Although the researchers were not able to find 100-percent-consistent brain activity in decision-making, their study does show that we subconsciously process all of our options before we make a decision.[xix]

Intuition

Intuition is another way that humans make decisions, although it might not be considered a rational thought process. It seems to appear spontaneously, but actually it's the result of subconscious brain functions like emotional processing, interpretation of nonverbal social cues, and our awareness of our own responses. This is why people often have a "bad feeling" about dangerous people they encounter, like killers— although they can't consciously put a finger on what is off about a person, nonverbal cues and emotional intelligence tell them that this person is bad news.

You can also subconsciously work out an answer to a problem that initially looks like it should be tackled with rational thought. This is why mathematicians often find the answers to difficult problems while taking a break from their work, or why you might find that you remember the answer to something while you're in the shower. Our brain works on the problems we want to solve subconsciously, even when we aren't consciously thinking of them. Once the brain finds the answer, it sends it to the conscious brain, making it seem like it came out of nowhere.

Changes in the brain

Changes in different areas of the brain can dramatically affect the decision-making process. In most brains, all the different parts have input in your choices. However, if you're missing a part of your brain, that part will not be able to take part in the decisions, and therefore the decisions will be different. Two scientists named Sophie Sowden and Caroline Catmur published research on this in 2013. They conducted an experiment to test decision-making brain activity by temporarily blocking the right temporo-parietal junction in a method called transcranial magnetic stimulation, or TMS. Blocking this junction cut off the part of the brain that recognizes that other people have intentions, and therefore allows us to predict their behavior. This is very important from an evolutionary standpoint, but it is also important to our moral judgment. When Sowden and Catmur blocked this pathway, they found that there was a negative impact on people's ability to make moral decisions about things like whether someone was guilty of a misdeed based on their intent. Another group of researchers also found that in patients who had strokes in the insular cortex (a part of the brain that controls cravings and, by extension, addiction) lost any previous addictions easily. These examples concern our physical responses and how they control our decisions through the brain, but the connection between the physical brain and neurological responses persists in other areas, too.[xx]

The Split Brain Experiment

For example, the "Split Brain experiment," which was first conducted in the 1950s by Roger Sperry and Ronald Myers, led to the discovery that the different hemispheres of our brains control different functions. The subjects had all had their brains separated to prevent diseases, generally epilepsy, from migrating between different parts of the brain. This separation allowed the researchers to test how much of our "consciousness" each hemisphere can control. Sperry and Myers found that in a split brain, the behaviors stored in one hemisphere did not transfer to the other one. Instead, each hemisphere of the brain operated independently.

The experiments were set up in the following manner: patients were asked to look at a screen that was divided by a black dot in the center, so each side of the brain would only take in the inputs that its respective eye could transmit (each hemisphere could only process information from one eye). Since each hemisphere processes information from the eye on the side of the head opposite to it, the right hemisphere processed what was on the left of the screen and the left hemisphere processed what was to the right. When Sperry flashed a word on one side of the screen and asked patients what it was, they were able to analyze and remember it with their left hemisphere, but not the right. This led Sperry to conclude that the left hemisphere processes language. However, when he asked the group that processed the word with the right hemisphere to draw what the word represented (e.g., "apple" and drawing an apple), they could do it with their left hands (controlled by the right hemisphere). This means that the right hemisphere took in the information it saw, but it couldn't process it, and therefore the person could not draw the word. This, as well as some other similar experiments, led Sperry to maintain these conclusions, as well as the theory that people with "split brains" still lost some brain function even if they were not impaired, because their hemispheres could no longer communicate to process information.[xxi]

Our brain also controls whether or not we feel that we live inside our bodies, specifically behind the eyes (where, of course, the brain lives). This feeling is a constructed experience, and when our brains can't do it because of drugs or brain damage, we tend to have an out-of-body experience. Our sense of "ownership" of our bodies, for example the sense that your arm is your arm when you lift it, is also constructed by harmonious interaction between the brain's impulses and the muscles' ability to follow those impulses. When people suffer strokes or accidents that impair motor control, they often don't feel like the limb is theirs anymore, which leads to "alien limb syndrome." The opposite happens in the case of amputations; amputees often describe the sensation of a "phantom limb" at their amputation site because their brains and muscles are still connected there and expect to control the full limb. A team of researchers published findings in the New England Journal of Medicine that "mirror therapy," or being able to see amputated limbs move in a mirror while moving them, reduced pain from "phantom limb" phenomena. Although they were not able to pinpoint this phenomenon happened in neurological terms, it seems that having a visual provided by a mirror helped their brains adjust to the new sensory configuration of muscles and neurons.[xxii]

The Ideomotor Effect [xxiii]

The ideomotor effect involves a similar complex interplay between muscles, brain, and visual input. This is subconscious motor control. For example, you might walk to the store without remembering you were going there. Instead, you brain subconsciously guided your muscles to that destination without needing any conscious input. People often attribute supernatural causes to this effect, such as possession. However, this effect is completely natural, and just a result of the brain being able to compartmentalize motor function into subconscious processes.

Altered States of Consciousness

Altered states of consciousness can also make us aware of how different parts of our brain act at different times. For example, you might find that it's hard to draw while singing, or that you can't sketch while you dream. Drugs and alcohol also produce this sort of altered state. This is because they depress certain parts of the brain, especially the frontal lobe (which is involved in inhibitions and decision-making). Your judgment and social skills will decrease in an alcohol-fueled altered state, but you won't be able to tell why. These changes are subconscious, just like those in the split-brain experiments.

When we're hypnotized, we're also in a state of altered consciousness. Hypnosis entails a sense of heightened awareness, to the degree that the subject can realize things the conscious mind was not aware of. Sensory information is processed through purely sensory subconscious channels during hypnosis, which can also produce unusual effects. However, the brain can also do the opposite; when people give in to a cult leader, they give up the critically thinking part of their brain and refuse to process warning signs subconsciously. This is actually an evolved response; when people are either hypnotized or encounter a charismatic leader, their critical thinking gets turned off by the brain in favor of physical responses.

The brain is a complex organ. However, it is a physical organ, and therefore is subject to the chemical processes it produces. This is why humans do not have perfect self-control, and are subject to spur-of-the-moment decisions or bad self-control. People often fail when they try to consciously change their habits; this is because our brains have trouble readjusting their chemical balances and desires. The frontal lobe, which governs our decisions, uses a lot of energy, so we don't always use it when we should. Therefore, we are often at the mercy of our instincts.

This being said, we are capable of making decisions. In fact, being cognizant of our brain's pitfalls and weaknesses will help us to work through a critical thinking process. Even though we are subject to our habits and desires, this does not mean that we cannot change them. We can change your habits by changing your behavior and thinking, because doing this will change your brain over time. Critical thinking is one of the primary devices you can use to change your behavior. The brain is able to change physically and neurologically, which is a good sign in that we are able to train our brains. Once your brain knows how to use logical, empirical tools, you'll be able to apply them to all facets of your life, and therefore be able to avoid common pitfalls caused by the "primitive brain." The next few chapters will discuss how to develop these skills for better decision-making.

Chapter 4: Arguments and Logical Fallacies

The previous chapters described how many errors our brains are susceptible to by their very nature. However, there are several tools we can use to correct these tendencies. Our frontal lobes, which develop as we age, help us make well-reasoned decisions (this is why teenagers are so infamous for being impulsive). This part of the brain helps with logical arguments, which this chapter will discuss, as well as common flaws in logic called fallacies.

Well-constructed arguments will help you prove your point, but they will also help you communicate better with others. Remember, critical thinking is not about winning—it's about following closely the process of argument development in reaching your conclusions. With effective argumentative skills, you will be able to better determine what conclusions are true, as well as the logical merits of other people's arguments. Arguing well will help you learn, and ultimately refine your own beliefs and ideas.

Argumentative skills will also help you get used to reasoning through your ideas, instead of rationalizing them. Think of rationalizing as the root of confirmation bias; it is when you form a conclusion first, then come up with arguments to justify it. Reasoning, meanwhile, is the inverse of this. Reasoning entails gathering data, observations, and evidence to make a conclusion. Coincidentally, this is also how academics in every discipline put together their work, or at least should. Giving up rationalizing is difficult, because it helps us explain the decisions we've made (not necessarily thinking them through), which is comforting. Human brains don't like to be wrong, and every time people rationalize, their reward centers are hit with a shot of dopamine to validate their "correctness." However, opening up to the full potential of critical thinking and logical argument will help resolve any discomfort your brain feels when it's wrong. Once it has a process to reevaluate arguments, the brain becomes much more comfortable with potentially changing its ideas.

How Is an Argument Built Up?

When used in terms of logic, the argument is the set of statements you use to support your conclusion. Saying that something is true, or explaining why it is true, does not fully constitute an argument.

When we construct arguments, we start with specific premises, from which we derive a conclusion. We take premises as a given; these can be either a fact or assumption. If, when examining premises, we discover that a premise is false, we can conclude that the argument itself is unsound. Finding these premises is one of the most difficult aspects of assessing an argument but it's very important to do so. When people disagree, it's often because they are working with different premises, and unless they can find the exact premise where they differ, it is hard to resolve the disagreement.

It's fine to use assumptions as premises; the most important thing is recognizing that assumptions are not facts. This doesn't mean that they are wrong, but they are not necessarily true. They might not be complete or logically consistent. Therefore, you should not default to using assumptions in your arguments, because they are more likely to weaken arguments and lead to incorrect conclusions. Always try to use as many certain facts as you can.

When people disagree on what a fact is, one of the people has to be wrong. The same is true in the case of conclusions. If you find yourself disagreeing with someone on something you both regard as a fact, your interaction with them should not be focused on defending your "side." Instead, you should be prepared to dissect both of your arguments to see the root of the disagreement. One of you is working with erroneous logic. If you can work together to figure out where this error occurs, then eventually you will come to the correct conclusion (which might be one that neither of you have considered). Taking this approach is both more productive and better for relationships than defending your argument to the death.

Although it seems like the goal of constructing an argument is to find the truth, they are not necessarily true in themselves. Conclusions can be true or false, but since we don't have access to the truth in an absolute sense, we treat things as "true" when we have enough evidence to make them provable as a fact. However, these truths are always subject to reexamination; that is how society makes progress.

We use the term "valid" instead of "true" with respect to logic, because something can be logically well-reasoned without necessarily being true. If one of your premises is incorrect but your logic is not flawed, your argument, or logic, is valid. If your premises are true and your argument is valid, your conclusion is true. When this is the case, the argument is sound. However, even if an argument is not sound, it still might be true; it could be either true or false. For example, you could say that it's cold outside because the sun is in the sky less. Both of these things are true independently, but they do not have a causal relationship. Therefore, your logic is unsound with a true conclusion.

Deductive Logic[xxiv]

One of the most common types of logic is deductive logic, which is logic that uses a combination of premises to derive a conclusion. If you start with the premises that all trees have wood and your house has wood floors, you can deduce that your floors came from trees. Because both of the premises are true, your conclusion will also be true and your logic is sound. These conclusions are called "positive assertions," which means they are saying what something is, instead of what it is not.

Although logically deduced arguments, if sound, are true, this does not mean that they are judgments of value or aesthetic. You and a friend might disagree over whether opera is actually entertaining, or whether houseplants are a good decorating method. These judgments are subjective, and there is no "right" answer to the question of their truth. A failure to recognize this—in other words, to misconceive your opinions as objective truth—is at the root of most people's arguments and disagreements. When we are cognizant of this, we can "agree to disagree" and accept that people have different value and aesthetic judgments that are separate from logical truths.

Inductive Logic

Inductive logic is the inverse of deductive logic. This means that it decides what is true based on observation, and is therefore a good way to construct theories rather than facts. Inductive reasoning is similar to the reasoning used in the scientific method. The invention of penicillin derived from a scientist noting that the mold, penicillin, that had grown in a petri dish in his lab had killed the bacteria he was studying in the dish. From this observation and repetitions of the conditions, he used inductive reasoning to conclude that penicillin is an antibiotic. Penicillin is still a popular antibiotic today because there has been no evidence to refute its utility as an antibiotic, but if there were, people would reverse their thinking and stop using it to treat infections. Inductively reasoned conclusions are always subject to revision in light of new observations; this example just happens to be one of a particularly strong evidence-based claim.

Non Sequitur Logic or Invalid Logic[xxv]

Think about the logic of this statement:

All A are B.

B is A.

Therefore, C is B.

This doesn't make sense as an argument, but why? If the two premises are true, then anything A also has to be B, and anything B is A. But neither of these premises have C in them. It is impossible to argue, therefore, that C is B based on the stated premises, and the argument is invalid. This is an example of a logical fallacy, because it is not a mathematical truth derived from the logical process. There are many different types of fallacies, but this one is called a non sequitur. "Non sequitur" is Latin for "does not follow," and is exactly what it sounds like—when a conclusion is unrelated to the premises. Some of the other types of logical fallacies are explained below.

Types of Logical Fallacies

- Arguments from authority[xxvi]

Arguments from authority are the "because I said so" argument; the argument that just because someone is in charge, their argument is correct. This type of fallacy can also apply to people who seem believable just because they have traits perceived as positive; for example, "Shelly volunteers at a shelter and is a good person, therefore what she believes about organic food is right." The darkest side of this fallacy is often found in cults, where people fall prey to the tendency to believe people in authority who are charismatic. People evolved to want to exist in cohesive social groups where they can follow a leader. This respect helps keep society together, but it cannot override rational thinking.

Arguments from authority are an easy fallacy to fall into because of our evolved need to follow a leader. However, other fallacies stem from various other impulses. They allow us to rationalize something that isn't true, by using false assumptions or premises, or by following invalid logic. Fallacies are the defense mechanism the brain uses when it wants to feel right and validated in its conclusions.

Arguments from authority are also a common counterargument; many good arguments, such as Galileo's argument that the solar system is heliocentric, have been shot down using arguments from authority. Of course, just because an authority makes an argument does not mean that argument is incorrect. Experts don't need to be blindly followed, but if their evidence is good, it is wise to consider their arguments. This is why the scientific method and peer academic review exist: to reach a consensus that is as close to the truth as possible. Therefore, one has to be careful when claiming argument from authority; authorities like expert scientists often have more going for them than just their leadership positions.

• Argument from final consequence

The chief feature of arguments from final consequence is that cause and effect are conflated—they start with an observable effect, and assume a cause for that effect. They often appear in the form of arguments like, "This conclusion can't be true, because I don't like the implications of it," or "This is true, because it supports a position I like." Creationists often use arguments from final consequence to affirm their beliefs that evolution can't be true, by arguing that people could not have come from animals they believe to be lower in the hierarchy of living beings. This is because the animals we evolved from don't have "morals," so we can't have acquired morals through evolution. However, a critical thinker can easily refute this by saying that just because animals don't have morality the way we do does not mean that we could not have evolved from them. These arguments are also teleological arguments, which is another way of saying that they're found by determining causes based on effects. This is often a mode of thinking used by historians to try to explain the modern world, but it is not a rigorous method of scientific thinking

Conspiracy theorists also tend to use arguments from final consequence. They like to think of world events in terms of who they benefit, or *qui bono*. This is how they argue that the moon landing was staged; the United States needed to get a man on the moon to get ahead in the space race, and since the technology wasn't given enough time to develop, the government must have faked it. Of course, there are always people who reap benefits from historical events, and in the case of the moon landing it was definitely the United States. However, they could have easily lost if the mission went wrong, and they lost several astronauts in accidents in their effort to develop the technology. The moon landing was a truly remarkable achievement, but this does not mean it has to be fake. Reaching such a conclusion is evidence of a logical fallacy.

- Post hoc ergo propter hoc

"Post hoc propter hoc" means "after that, on account of that" in Latin, and this fallacy is exactly what it sounds like. Just because X happened after Y, does not mean that Y caused X. This fallacy is especially potent when people do not know the intricacies of probability and statistics. For example, a sociologist could notice that the crime rate in a city decreases when graffiti is cleaned up, and assume that the graffiti clean-up is what caused the result. However, it could be due to other factors like the weather, the raid of a drug ring, or something else.

Post hoc propter hoc is so appealing because as humans, it is in our nature to search for meaning in the events we observe. However, just because they happen in a certain order does not mean that their relationship is causal. People often confuse correlation for causation, but when one examines the logic behind this is clear that this is not a logically sound line of thinking. For example, imagine that X happened after Y, as was said in the previous paragraph. It is possible that Y caused X, but it is equally as possible that some other event, Z, caused X, or even both X and Y. There is not even necessarily a correlation; all these events' concurrence could be mere coincidence. There are many possibilities for the cause of X, and all the other ones (various circumstances of correlation, and coincidence) need to be tested before causation can be established. For example, right-winger Andrew Schlafly made this statement about abortion: "In Romania, abortion was illegal under two decades of rule by the communist dictator Nicolae Ceausescu, and the country enjoyed one of the lowest breast cancer rates in the entire world during that time, far lower than comparable Western countries."[xxvii]

There is no definitive and credible evidence that a lower rate of abortion has a direct correlation with a lower risk of breast cancer. This kind of correlation is not evidence of causation. A profound case control epidemiological study should examine the chance of the factors that may have been had real impact on breast cancer risk. Maybe smoking rates dropped or dieting habits changed. The reason could have been anything.

It is easy to spot a post hoc ergo propter hoc fallacy because they will rarely have any sort of credible evidence to support them. There might be correlation present, but this is not the same as causation. To determine causation, all confounding factors have to be removed—environmental, social, circumstantial—and an experiment has to be carefully conducted. This is why the scientific method is so important; much bad science, like the sociology experiment described earlier, is actually a result of this fallacy.

- Ad hoc or post hoc reasoning

Ad hoc or post hoc reasoning happens when people add erroneous reasoning to their theories to explain the nature of the evidence they have found. This reasoning does not have to be wrong in itself; rather, it is wrong in its application.

People who believe in the scientific veracity of ESP (extrasensory perception) also believe that skepticism prevents ESP from working. The believers, of course, created this explanation ad hoc to explain why ESP did not work in scientifically controlled studies. There was no reason *a priori* to believe skepticism blocked ESP before this problem arose, which is a key giveaway in the ad hoc fallacy.[xxviii]

Ad hoc reasoning helps people formulate theories, but it can't be used as a premise. There are plenty of untrue things that would be true if one premise were actually true, but creating such premises is not logically sound.

Conspiracy theorists also love ad hoc reasoning because it allows them to invent explanations for their theories after the theories are already developed. For example, the alien conspiracy theorist Billy Meier claimed that his doctored photos were the result of chance only *after* they were questioned as a hoax. Every time someone found a falsified element of his evidence, he had an explanation. These explanations were often ridiculous, such as his statement that aliens had moved a tree on his property to hide their identity after his photograph of a UFO was determined to contain a tree that didn't exist on his property. This is an extreme example of people creating evidence to support their theories, but ad hoc fallacies in general follow the same principle.[xxix]

- Ad hominem

Ad hominem logical fallacies occur in arguments that are directed toward the person who is making the opposing argument, rather than the elements of the argument itself. This is the counterpart of the argument from authority, because it rejects an argument based on the negative qualities of the person making it instead of accepting it based on the merits of the person arguing it. People often respond to skeptics using the ad hominem argumentative fallacy, saying that they are close-minded or do not have open minds. However, this does not preclude accepting good arguments, and ignores that the skeptic might just have an exceptional reasoning process. Indeed, the "close-minded" skeptic might actually be quite open-minded, and just averse to claims that are not properly supported by logic or evidence. Thus, ad hominem attacks often shut out people who are the best critical thinkers.

Ad hominem fallacies also occur when people reject arguments based on their personal dislike or impression of someone, for example the perception that a scientist is arrogant. People also often reject rigorous evidence for things like climate change on the grounds that scientists are "elitist." Similarly, people also often resort to the ad hominem attack that the people they disagree with are supported by big corporations, or some shady wing of the government. Of course, people do have conflicts of interest, but assuming these often leads to falling into the ad hominem fallacy, and at worst to wild and dangerous conspiracy theories.

Insulting someone personally is not in itself an example of the ad hominem fallacy. Instead, this personal insult has to be used to invalidate evidence to fall under the fallacy. People make mistakes and have personal flaws, but this does not necessarily mean their evidence is untrue.

A related category of fallacy is called poisoning the well, wherein people try to "poison" someone's argument by associating it with an unpopular concept. "Godwin's law" is an example of this—it's the idea that the longer an argument persists on the Internet, the more likely it is something or someone will be compared to Hitler or the Nazis. Anti-vaxxers have often resorted to comparing mandatory vaccines to Nazi eugenics programs in their online arguments, in a clear example of this phenomenon.[xxx]

Of course, pointing out someone's flaws can be a worthy way to invalidate their argument; for example, if that person claims to not be a racist and then is revealed to support racist rhetoric, their standing as an anti-racist is invalidated. In another example, if someone has run a scam before, it is fair to refuse to invest in their new company. This is not poisoning the well; rather, it is working from a well-reasoned thought process based on real evidence.

- Argumentum ad ignorantiam

Argumentum ad ignorantiam is exactly what it sounds like—it is the practice of creating evidence for a conclusion based on a *lack* of knowledge. For example, alien conspiracy theorists will often claim that aliens made crop circles because they do not know if a person made them. Because there is no specific human actor, they immediately jump to aliens as being the cause instead of considering other possibilities or admitting that the cause is unknown. Creationists also argue using this fallacy. They believe that because scientists do not have evidence of a "missing link," the "intelligent designer" (most often God) must have created people. This explanation compensates for the gap in their knowledge; however, it is not actually evidence, because there is no hard evidence for the process of intelligent design, either.

More broadly, this fallacy is a characteristic component of conspiracy theories. People are attracted to conspiracy theories because they can fill gaps in people's knowledge, such as why JFK was assassinated or why the police destroyed evidence in the years following RFK's assassination. People often look for things that seem out of place in the chronology of events and then fill in the holes they see with their own theories. There is generally little to no positive evidence for these theories, which is why the conspiracies developed in the first place. This lack of evidence is what makes an argument fall under this fallacy.

- False dichotomy

Imagine that you are trying to determine why a soup you're cooking doesn't taste right. You guess that it's either because you didn't add enough salt, or because you haven't kept it on the stove long enough, and fiddle with both of those options to see if they solve the problem. However, neither of these options fixed the soup. It was impossible to solve the problem this way because it was reasoned using a false dichotomy, or the idea that there are only two choices for an answer when in fact there could be many more options. People often fall into this trap in popular debate on issues like "nature versus nurture," or whether genes or upbringing have more of an influence on people's personalities. Epigenetics is a rapidly growing field that suggests a third answer that is a combination of the two, making it clear that this debate stems from a false dichotomy.

False dichotomies are dangerous because they can reduce a spectrum of possible answers to a question to two polarized answers. With respect to sexuality, for example, people only realized recently that there were more sexualities than just gay or straight. In fact, most people lie somewhere along the spectrum, and at some point have been attracted to multiple genders or no one at all. There is also a fallacy called false continuum that is the inverse of this; just because there is a continuum does not mean extremes do not exist. There are some people who only like people of the same gender, and some people who only like members of the opposite gender. However, these are not the only two types of people in the world.

False dichotomies are seductive because they appeal to people's desire for clarity and simplicity in their worldview. Therefore, it is important to keep them in mind and never restrict possible answers to just two options. This practice can rule out a lot of good ideas.

- Moving the goalpost

"Moving the goalpost" is not a formal logical fallacy the way an *ad hominem* argument is, but it is still important to keep in mind. This happens when the parameters for making an argument are changed after a conclusion is reached for no good reason. People who view argumentation as competition often use this tactic to try to "win," or at least not "lose," an argument. The "goalposts" can move so far that eventually remaining within their parameters is no longer possible. Notably, this has been a problem in the right-wing birther conspiracy theories about President Barack Obama. When the conspiracy theorists demanded to see Obama's birth certificate, he released it. When they complained that this was not the original full certificate, Obama went to the state of Hawaii and had that one released. After being confronted with this irrefutable evidence, the conspiracy theorists demanded more and more of Obama's records from his time in high school, college, and even his mother's life. Many other conspiracy theorists use the same tactics, such as moon-landing conspiracy theorists who always demand high-resolution photo evidence of increasingly higher standards as NASA releases more photographs.

Fortunately, this fallacy is rather easy to identify. Although it is good to seek more evidence, moving the goalposts is in a different category because its goals are to discredit their opponents to the point where they demand standards that are impossible to meet. The best way to deal with this strategy, therefore, is to eventually walk away and let the evidence speak for itself. This fallacy is often a sign of argumentative desperation.

- Strawman fallacy

The final fallacy discussed in this chapter is also one that is popularly used on the Internet— the strawman fallacy. This is a tactic where someone will respond to a version of their opponent's argument that they have altered for their convenience. The idea is that this new version will be easier to defeat, just like a strawman as opposed to a real soldier. This is another tactic that people use when they argue to win, rather than argue to learn. For example, in political debates, people who advocate for criminal justice reform, such as lighter drug sentencing, are often confronted with the strawman, "So you want our streets to be ridden with drugs and crime?" This is not what the criminal justice reform advocates are arguing, but it's an easier position for opponents to take down. In another example, if a school board proposes using new funds to replace drafty building windows, opponents using the strawman fallacy might respond, "So you don't want to invest in more security measures to keep our schools safe?"

The strawman fallacy can be appealing in settings where emotions get the best of people.

Still, it is important to be cognizant that argumentation is about finding a solution, not winning. If you find yourself arguing with someone based on things they never said they believed, you are resorting to strawman tactics, and might want to reexamine your arguments.

In Conclusion

Arguments are helpful because they allow humans to articulate their different opinions and solve them. The goal of an argumentative debate should always be to find any underlying fallacies or faulty premises, not to destroy the other side. Remember, beliefs are subject to change with the proper evidence, and that includes *your* beliefs. Examine the arguments you make and see if you're falling into any of the fallacies described above as a form of self-examination and self-improvement. This will also help augment your critical thinking skills, and ultimately make it easier to reach conclusions that are well-reasoned and supported by evidence.

Chapter 5: On Marketing, Media, and Other Mind Games

Think about how many emails you get a day. Lots of them are emails from stores with small sales, promotions, or free delivery from your favorite restaurant. Or there might be emails from your college alumni association to ask for donations, or from your favorite magazines with a list of articles you might like. All of these emails are trying to get you to do something—whether it's buying new shoes, ordering delivery, donating to your college, or reading the magazine. There is probably fine print, but you don't read it. You read what the people sending the email want you to read.

Forms of marketing, advertising, propaganda, and persuasion have existed since people could communicate with each other. However, the existence of the Internet has changed the game. The Internet has provided easier access to more information than people have ever known before, and with this access has come democratization. Our information is also less edited and processed than it ever has been before, and this means that every opinion, bias, and point of view gets equal exposure on the Internet regardless of intellectual merit. Critical thinking skills are crucial to navigating this new environment of unfiltered information. With fewer editors to mediate content, people now need to do the mediation for themselves. Critical thinking helps in the decision-making process when choosing which information to believe.

Spam Emails

The "junk" or "spam" filter in email often hosts a variety of scams. Some are more than annoying; they are openly malicious. They often look like this:

"Dear Sir.

I have gone through your file and my extensive investigation confirmed that you are the original beneficiary shortlisted to receive this fund but only the total sum of Seven Million United States Dollars ($7,000,000.00 USD) was approved for payment."

This kind of message will often be followed by a request for personal information, like bank account or social security numbers.

These scams are very common. Many people call them the "Nigerian scam" after the country where the email form originated, or the "419 scam" after its number in the Nigerian criminal code. These have existed since the 1920s in the form of letters, but the Internet has enabled mass dissemination on an unprecedented scale. These scams generate as much as five billion dollars a year in revenue. They also rely on victims' financial greed and desperation, as well as gullibility. Once people answer the email, scammers will continue to solicit money from them as long as they can, charging fees or claiming that bribes need to be paid. Sometimes, scammers even ask people to travel to a different country and then kidnap them, extorting money from their families. This is just one of the dangers of a lack of Internet awareness.

"Fake News" Emails

These emails often appear as chain emails, and you might have seen one; for example, one that says, "A hacker has been friending people you know. If he friends one of your friends, he will be able to hack into your Messenger. His profile picture is of a red car. PROTECT YOURSELF do not accept his friend request." Sometimes these scams have roots in truth, but they have been so distorted as to be completely counterfactual. They are designed to spread virally through the Internet, shared by people who fall for them.

One of these emails was one that circulated among the ultra-right wing and Islamophobic part of the Internet—it was a "mass wedding" in Gaza of men in their twenties to brides who were only ten years old or younger. There were photographs attached of young girls, and they were from a real Hamas wedding in Gaza—but the girls were guests and relatives, not the brides themselves. Most of the brides, in fact, were eighteen, and the youngest was sixteen—within the legal minimum marriage age (with parental consent) in many U.S. states. However, without bothering to check the facts, many right-wingers took the original story as fact and posted about it on their blogs and forums, stoking anti-Muslim sentiments.

There were many signs that this story was false: the language had a clear emotional bias, and the story lacked links to a reputable source for its information. The pictures are also without context; none actually show any ceremonies taking place, and instead are just photographs of groups of people. Furthermore, no global news outlets reported the story. These should all provoke skepticism in the critical thinker, and online research would prove that the story was a hoax. However, lots of people don't even take the step of Googling something to make sure it's true. If you receive an email with content that seems suspicious in its factuality, it is always helpful to ask someone you know about the topic, and see if you have a reason to be wary of that information.

The Burger Myth[xxxi]

You might have heard the story that fast food hamburgers have so many preservatives in them, you could leave one out for months or even years and it would not go bad. This is actually an urban legend known as the "burger myth," and was promoted by several healthy-living "mommy bloggers" who refused to feed them to their children. One journalist decided to test this claim by conducting an experiment using the scientific method because this had not been done previously. He first came up with several hypotheses about what caused the burgers to remain fresh, and eliminated them until he decided to test the theory that the beef did not rot because of its material. To test this claim, he purchased his own ground beef and made homemade burgers to use as control subjects. He took several types of McDonald's burgers and made homemade counterparts to them, then left all of them out, testing them every day for mold. He found that *none* of the burgers had significantly rotted—even the no-salt burger (salt acts as a preservative). However, the Quarter Pounders showed the most signs of mold, leading him to conclude that their larger size meant they dried out faster, giving mold, which requires moisture, more time to grow.

What does all this mean? *Any* burger that is cooked properly will have some self-preserving properties. People have been salting, drying, and storing meat without refrigerators or freezers for thousands of years. Preservation is a function of dryness, rather than chemicals that are only present in fast food.

There are many claims like this on the Internet, in all corners of different communities. It is impossible to describe them all but fortunately they can all be assessed in the same way. Critical thinking processes provide an interpretive guide to the wild information found online, and these steps will help separate fact from fiction.

The first thing anyone should consider with respect to online information is its source. Does the website it comes from have a clear political or ideological bias? Is it an independent publication? Is it highly emotional in tone? Is it run by amateurs, or professional journalists and academics who have to follow professional ethical guidelines? These are all important in determining whether a website is trustworthy.

The case of the burger illustrates how important it is to consider all implications of a claim as well. If burgers are so dangerous, why haven't any scientists or governmental authorities banned them? What about the international community? Radio silence from the experts on a topic can indicate that the information is not factual.

Finally, see if there is any sort of consensus on the topic in reputable sources. Read several websites run by the experts listed above to find any patterns and other sources for information. Once you find the "original source" where people are getting their information, read that. If all these sources say the same thing, it is generally fair to judge the claim reliable and reasonably truthful.

Marketing Scams

There is a whole industry built on exploiting people's brain chemistry, cognition, and biases to get them to buy things: marketing. This entire field developed around the idea that there are specific strategies that will get people to spend money on things they don't necessarily need.

One of these strategies is 99-cent pricing. Humans exhibit something called the left-digit effect, where the leftmost digit of a price influences how we perceive that price more than the other digits. Since we perceive something that costs $19.99 as significantly cheaper than something that costs $20.00 (even though it isn't), we're more likely to buy the item at $19.99. Researchers have proposed that this effect arises from the human brain's limits in terms of the amount of information it can process; in other words, people's tendency to prefer simple information over complicated ideas.[xxxii]

Another classic marketing strategy is to manipulate people based on their need for self-esteem and to appear competent to others.

Salespeople will often use tactics such as asking leading questions about their product's quality or how much you like it to get you to agree and ultimately trick you into believing what you say about the product. If it seems like you like the product, you'll want to appear consistent to the salesperson, and therefore you're likely to buy it. This is an easy way to manipulate emotions to get you to buy something that is unnecessary, or that you don't even like.

Of course, most of our decisions to buy things are not made using rational thought processes. Instead, they're often made subconsciously. Marketers tap into these "impulse buys" to goad us into buying their products. In fact, around 80 percent of luxury items and 60 percent of food purchases are impulse buys! Psychology plays a huge role in this phenomenon. The anchoring heuristic, or the idea that our minds are attached to a higher price than the one shown, is one tactic; this is why stores often have items marked as on sale, even though there isn't a large price difference, or have price comparison tools. Stores also provide services like money-back guarantees to counter buyer's remorse because they actually make people more sure that they are satisfied with their purchases and took less of a risk in buying them.

Marketers are also good at inventing problems for consumers to worry about. Think of the marketing for the expensive security camera monitoring systems that are becoming more common; ads often play during true crime television shows or podcasts, and tell you that "this is the way you can protect yourself," even though you have a slim-to-nonexistent chance of being murdered by a serial killer. The alarm company has manufactured a fear, and made it seem real thanks to placement in an entertainment program about real events. This makes you forget that such events are rare, and makes you think that the key to assuaging this manufactured fear is to buy the product.

MLMs

You might have recently received a message from an old college or high school acquaintance telling you about an exciting new business opportunity where you can "be your own boss" or "set your own hours" selling products like makeup, health supplements, workout gear, or knives. This is how many people first encounter multi-level marketing or MLMs, a scam that has proliferated over social media. It is especially important to be aware of the dangers and practices of MLMs, because they are essentially pyramid schemes dressed in the clothing of a legitimate business.

In MLMs, salespeople make money by recruiting salespeople under them, because each person gets a cut of the profits made by their sub-employees. People pay for their own products and then have to pay back their investment by selling them to others. If they do not make back the money they've invested, they cannot advance up the ranks. Every salesperson therefore has to recruit people under them just to keep their heads above water. Of course, this is not a sustainable business model; after about 15 levels, every person on the planet would have to be involved in an MLM to keep it going! This is similar to the phenomenon of pedigree collapse, where intermarriage reduces the size of a family tree until the family collapses, as seen in the famous case of the Habsburg royal dynasty, who eventually died out due to incest. [xxxiii] The rapid saturation of salespeople makes the continuation of the scheme impossible.

MLMs are extremely manipulative in their tactics. They turn their own customers into a salesforce, which makes them very loyal by tricking them into thinking the product they're selling is great (remember, no one wants to be a sucker). Around 95 percent of MLM salespeople never make their money back, and in fact lose money, because they are unable to offload their merchandise to people outside of the network and instead become their own customers. MLMs often force people to buy a minimum amount of merchandise which can also make it difficult to ever get out of debt. However, because there *are* people at the top of the pyramid, people are deluded into thinking that they, too can make it, even if that is extremely unlikely.

Many MLMs are essentially quack pharmacies, selling medical or health-related products that either don't work or are actively dangerous. However, they trick people into buying these products by making statements about their effectiveness that are too good to be true, like immunity-boosting properties or instant weight loss without any effort. Of course, if these things were possible, they would be all over the media and everyone would know about them. However, they counter these claims by advancing conspiracy theories of suppression by pharmaceutical companies or the government.

Instead of science, these products therefore often rely on personal testimony as an advertising strategy. People have evolved to find other people's stories captivating; we are social animals, after all, and stories often prove more enticing than lab reports. However, they are nowhere near as accurate. Some MLMs will also claim their products are scientifically verified by professionals, which is an effective strategy, but will actually lack the evidence to back these claims up. Therefore, the most popular strategies are still personal testimonials and distortion of effects. Fortunately, critical thinking is an evaluative tool that is particularly effective against the false claims and strategies used by MLMs, and therefore you will be able to protect yourself.

Chapter 6: Conspiracy Theories De-Mystified

Introduction

If you were asked to name a conspiracy theory right now, it would be easy to think of one, right? For example, the theory that the Mafia or the CIA assassinated JFK, or that the government knew about 9/11 and even engineered it to have a reason to invade Iraq, or that the moon landing was actually filmed on a movie set. Many people believe in at least one of these theories even though they are not seen as credible by mainstream journalists and scholars. Why is this?

Everyone is a bit of a conspiracy theorist at heart. People love the idea that broad organizations are what is keeping them from achieving their goals, instead of their own flaws and mistakes. This is because humans developed pattern-recognition traits as an evolutionary tool to aid in survival; in small doses, this is extremely useful, but it can become destructive when it gets out of hand. Some people organize their entire lives around conspiracy theories and are completely consumed by them. My grandfather was a Second World War veteran and to the day of his death he was suspicious of our German neighbor being a Nazi and secretly plotting to reignite the flame of the belief. He spent hours in a row peeking out the window looking at what the neighbor did, when did he leave the house, when did he return, with whom did he speak, and at the end of the day my grandfather shared his insights as "discoveries" with the family. Every person the German neighbor spoke with became instantly suspicious in my grandfather's eyes. It wasn't long before the entire neighborhood became "unsafe."

Yet he didn't want to move anywhere else as "someone had to keep an eye" on the neighbor. Luckily, my grandfather was never violent and his conspiracy theory didn't leave the house. In the eyes of the world he was the poor British veteran with severe PTSD.

My grandfather's little conspiracy theory is considered a minor one as it had only one proponent, him and the German neighbor. Any of the conspiracy theories at the beginning of this chapter qualify as "grand conspiracies," or conspiracy theories that involve large organizations or several governments (or some combination of both) working together over a long period of time. Grand conspiracies generally think of the world in terms of three types of people:

1. The conspirators, who are evil, extremely powerful, and have almost infinite resources at their disposal. Despite all

these resources, however, they are careless and make frequent slips that provide clues to their existence and agenda.

2. The conspiracy theorists, who are the only people who can see the conspirators for who they are. They are "brilliant" enough to put together the clues the conspirators leave behind, and often think of themselves as Messiahs who can save the world.

3. The naïves. That is to say, people who neither participate in nor investigate these conspiracies.

These conspiracy theories are often anti-Semitic; for example, the idea that Jewish people control all the money and governments in the world, or that the Rothschild family is secretly head of the "Illuminati" who control every institution on earth. People think these groups reveal themselves through symbols like the all-e or the triangle, which are extremely

place and used by organizations like the

sons, who people then form theories about.

common pieces of iconography are

ormed in the conspiracy theorists' minds into

evidence that certain groups of people or

anizations control the institutions that use

em. This sounds ridiculous, so why is it so

eductive?

Why Humans Love Thinking in Conspiracies

You might have noticed that conspiracy theorists who were once considered fringe, like Alex Jones, have become more popular over the last decade or so. In 1966, Richard Hofstadter presaged much of today's prevalence of conspiracies in his book *The Paranoid Style in American Politics.* Hofstadter believed that conspiracies were a type of psychopathology, almost like a mental illness that caused paranoid delusions. However, he could not explain wha made this pathology so appealing. The answer lie in people's need for control. Many fans of well-known conspiracy theorists like Jones are the type of people who feel powerless in the rapidly changing modern world. Furthermore, in an age where so much news is condensed into easily digested soundbites, people are more likely to fill in the holes in their knowledge with conspiracies. This feeds the human need to feel certain and secure about one's place in the world.

Pattern Recognition and Psychology

Conspiracy theories often hinge on human tendencies toward pattern recognition as well. After all, conspiracies are just elaborately constructed pattern of events, with some causality from a larger organization added in. Creating patterns is also a common response to a perceived lack of agency or control in life, which makes conspiracies even more appealing to those who feel that way. Furthermore, conspiracy theories often help people build self-esteem, by making them feel more knowledgeable and important to the wider world. They also serve as a conduit for emotions like anger or despair, which is part of the reason why conspiracies about JFK's assassination were so popular in the months and years following it; it was a huge wound on the American national psyche. Conspiracies give a sense of belonging, as well as the impression that one is special, which is a heady mix for most people, especially the disenfranchised.

Pattern Recognition vs. Reality Testing

When brains recognize patterns, they initiate a process called "reality testing" to process it. Reality testing is exactly what it sounds like: it is the brain trying to figure out whether a pattern is plausible within the existing reality it has already constructed. Does it seem rational, logical, and plausible within the context of what the brain already knows? For many people, the response to reality testing of conspiracies is a resounding "no." However, there are also groups of people for whom conspiracy theories conform quite well with their existing reality. There is a wide range of pattern-recognition and reality-testing paradigms in the human brain, subject to many different factors. For example, people with mental illnesses like schizophrenia have less-rigorous reality testing than people without the illness, because their brain chemistry diminishes their ability to perceive and process the reality people without the illness recognize. Therefore, people with hallucinatory or delusionally patterned mental illnesses tend to be more susceptible to conspiracy theories, although not all conspiracy theorists have such an illness.

How conspiracy theorists think is also the result of several other "cognitive traps" in the way the brain works. Confirmation bias, for example, is a big part of conspiratorial thinking, because it is the brain's tendency to cherry-pick the evidence that supports a foregone conclusion. Any information to the contrary is either ignored or unfairly discounted. Conspiracy theorists generally exhibit a lot of confirmation bias because they prefer ambiguous or shadowy evidence to support their claims instead of scientific or legal evidence. Furthermore, confirmation bias makes it difficult to change conspiracy theorists' minds; once they latch on to a theory, it is very difficult to get them to let go.

Another common cognitive error among conspiracy theorists is the fundamental attribution error, which is attributing people's behavior to their personal character or other internal factors, instead of on situations. Human actions are not always well-planned or intentional, and many things are a result of coincidence, but conspiracy theorists don't see things that way. Instead, they think that every action and circumstance is the result of elaborate planning. So, for example, they believe that Bush did 9/11 because he was not in Washington, DC that day, when in fact this was a scheduling quirk and pure coincidence.

Conspiracy theories often develop into "closed belief systems," or ones that can't be changed based on evidence and arguments that refute them. This is because their beliefs and cognitive processes evolve to defend their ideas from outside dissent instead of being receptive to other information. Anything that would contradict their beliefs is dismissed as untrue or twisted into further evidence of the beliefs themselves being true; for example, RFK conspiracists often accept that Sirhan Sirhan was the assassin, but that he was being mind-controlled by a larger organization. These practices help the conspiracy theorists isolate themselves within their own belief systems, and make it more difficult to break them out of them.

Furthermore, theorists are notorious for moving the goalposts required to prove something, as well as alienating themselves from the burden of proof in an argument. Shifting the burden of proof means that it is up to the person arguing with the conspiracy theorist to prove the conspiracy false, rather than the conspiracy theorist having to prove it is true. Otherwise, the conspiracy theorist will take their claim's truth for granted. Even if there is sufficient evidence to prove them wrong, the conspiracy theorist might also move the goalpost to invalidate that evidence; in other words, arbitrarily declaring that it's not good enough and doesn't meet their standard of proof anymore. This, of course, is a logical fallacy, but it is also an insulating tactic for the conspiracy theorist's belief system. Even if you try to explain every aspect of why the moon landing is real to them, they will still come up with details that "don't make sense" and validate their views, like that the flag moved when they placed it in the ground (even though this aspect of the theory has been solidly debunked by science), or that something was wrong with the video feed in a way that means it was on Earth, or that Stanley Kubrick once made a strange remark about the event. These "holes" are not rigorous evidence that the conspiracy theorist is right, but they will cling to them because they validate their views. This is a large part of what makes reasoning with conspiracy theorists such a frustrating experience.

Conspiracy theorists also like to latch on to the quirks and unusual events that happened in history at the same time as their pet topic—think of Jack Ruby shooting Lee Harvey Oswald. They then use these events to contradict people who try to argue with them, without actually having to come up with any evidence of the conspiracy itself. However, history is full of strange events—this is how the world works. There are coincidences all the time! This is part of something called "the law of large numbers," where the number of events and circumstances happening in the world every day is so large that strange things are bound to happen. Anomalies, therefore, don't actually say anything about any larger patterns or sinister organizational plots going on. Conspiracy theorists like to think that they have deeper meaning (which, of course, feeds into their tendency toward confirmation bias), but they really do not.

All these logical fallacies and cognitive errors culminate in the false dichotomy fallacy. This is essentially the synthesis of all the things conspiracy theorists find through the process detailed in the above paragraphs. Given all this "evidence," the conspiracy theorist will draw a false dichotomy between the commonly accepted narrative and their own concocted theory in order to put them on the same level and invalidate the common narrative. This only serves to reinforce their preexisting worldview.

Widening the Conspiracy

Conspiracy theorists often make their conspiracies larger in response to criticism as well. Think of this as the inverse of moving the goalposts. In response to criticism that no reporter ever found evidence that the Mafia assassinated JFK, for example, conspiracy theorists will respond that the media were in on it as well. If they are asked about investigation by the CIA or the FBI, they will simply widen the net to include those organizations as well. The larger these conspiracies become, however, the harder they become to support. Why would Cuban agents and the CIA cooperate to assassinate JFK if they were sworn geopolitical enemies? In the case of the moon landing, wouldn't the Soviets, with their extensive spy network, have caught on to the fact that the most important milestone in the "Space Race" was faked? Eventually, the conspiracies become so elaborate that they entail the collaboration of parties that would never have worked together. This seems implausible to the average non-conspiracist, but conspiracy theorists have a wide variety of tactics to protect and insulate their worldview from such implausibilities, as seen in the previous paragraphs.

What is the Harm in Coming Up with Conspiracy Theories?

Are conspiracy theories good for society, or bad? This might be surprising, but there actually is a scholarly debate on the topic.

Conspiracy theories can be good in that they serve as "gadflies" for society, sometimes pointing out real flaws in mainstream explanations. For example, RFK conspiracy theories have mostly served to highlight the need for better law enforcement cooperation between federal, state, and city authorities. They also serve as reminders of the need for transparency in government and private-sector action; secrecy in big institutions only adds fuel to conspiracy theorists' fires. This need can lead to freedom-of-speech and freedom-of-information laws that ultimately benefit society as a whole.

On the other hand, conspiracy theories can also lead to dangerous levels of mistrust of the government and democratic processes. Think of Alex Jones—his conspiracy theories, most prominently Birtherism, have undermined people's good faith in democracy and deeply divided the United States. The promulgation of such theories can actually lead people to argue for stricter restrictions on speech and information because of their dangers. Furthermore, people can lean too hard the other way from conspiracy theorists and accept mainstream narratives without asking any questions. Reasonable lines of questioning hold governments accountable, and can even help uncover corruption or misconduct in powerful institutions. Conspiracy theories actively discourage the practice of healthy skepticism because they make any questioning look fringe, illogical, unreasonable, and dangerous. Therefore, it's clear to have a solid understanding of what is and is not a conspiracy theory.

Conspiracy Theories That Were Actually True

Despite the fact that most conspiracy theories are not trustworthy, there are some that did turn out to be true! The following are listed in a *Reader's Digest* article as actually having happened:

- Late in Woodrow Wilson's second term, there were rumors that the President had suffered a stroke that prevented him from governing, so the First Lady took care of most official business. Edith Wilson, his young wife, did indeed take care of most of his business for several months after he had a stroke, but the government kept the whole thing quiet out of fear of political instability. Although Edith always said that she had only acted as a sort of secretary, most historians agree that she was essentially acting as President by reviewing state matters.

- People theorized that in the early years of the Cold War, the U.S. government was stealing dead bodies to do testing on the effects of nuclear fallout. This really did happen—in an operation called Project SUNSHINE, government agents collected the body parts of dead children and infants from around the world for testing, without notifying or asking permission from their families.

- Government mind-control conspiracy theories are common, but there was a real CIA project called MK-ULTRA that did actually focus on mind control. In the 1960s, the government recruited test subjects to experiment with LSD to attempt mind control. Eventually, it started dosing people who did not volunteer, and many people suffered permanent brain damage as a result.

- In the 1960s, many people also theorized that the FBI was spying on people like John Lennon, Martin Luther King Jr., and the Black Panthers. As it turns out, all these people and groups actually *were* under surveillance for being "subversive" figures who participated in, among other things, radical activism, the antiwar movement, and civil rights activism. This was part of an organized operation called CONINTELPRO that was created by J. Edgar Hoover in 1956. However, this sort of monitoring still goes on; there is evidence that the FBI has been monitoring activists in the Black Lives Matter movement as well.

- It is now a commonly accepted fact that tobacco smoking causes cancer, but once the Surgeon General declared smoking a health hazard, people began to theorize that the tobacco companies had already known about the link for years. This was indeed true; companies had access to research about the dangers of tobacco since the 1950s, but did not begin to admit that the research was correct until the 1990s.

The television show *Mad Men* deals extensively with the collaboration between advertisers and tobacco companies to hide the truth in the early 1960s.

- A Canadian conspiracy theory stated that their government was so concerned about gay people "infiltrating" government bureaucracy that they developed an actual "gaydar" test. This is true—the government hired a scientist in the 1960s to develop a machine that tested whether potential civil, military, or police employees' pupils widened when they viewed homoerotic imagery. The Canadian government fired or refused to hire hundreds of people as a result of this test.

- Some people have theorized that the Dalai Lama is a CIA agent. Well, he is on their payroll! The CIA paid him around $180,000 as part of their funding of the Tibetan resistance movement against the

Chinese government in the 1960s. This was meant to hamper and disrupt the influence of Communism in the country.

- Since the rapid expansion of the Internet and social media, people have been paranoid that the government has been watching people's online activity. As it turns out, the government filed tens of thousands of requests for user data from Facebook, Google, and Apple in 2016 alone. The Patriot Act authorized the NSA to monitor and collect almost everything on the Internet. Of course, this has only fueled popular speculation about Russian hackers influencing the 2016 Presidential election, which at the time of writing is still under investigation.[xxxiv]

Conclusion

Conspiracy theories are appealing because they fill many different human psychological needs. They don't adhere to logical principles; instead, they rely on cognitive biases, fallacies, and errors in people's perception of reality. Conspiracy theorists also use circular arguments to insulate themselves from criticism. It is important to remain vigilant about your own beliefs and ideas. Do you find yourself isolating yourself from evidence that doesn't support what you think, or that you simple don't like? Remember, anyone can be a conspiracy theorist; despite what movies and TV often show, conspiracies are not limited to people wearing tinfoil hats.

Therefore, think about whether your thinking is tending toward that of a conspiracy theorist. Do you feel like broader forces are working against you or the institutions you hold dear? Is this a logically reasonable thing to think? After all, it is true that 9/11 was the result of a radicalized Islamist conspiracy, but the U.S. wasn't involved—it just missed many warning signs because of lack of cooperation between different intelligence agencies. Al Qaeda was a real conspiracy, but not a grand conspiracy. Think about grand conspiracies as a sort of pseudoscience—they resemble real things that do happen, but they're the contaminated result of bad logic. If you encounter a conspiracy theory, it is therefore important to apply rigorous logical thinking to it. Ask yourself if the conspiracy really follows from the evidence, and what it would entail if it were true. Healthy skepticism is the most important tool you can use when dealing with conspiracy theories; it is excellent at filtering out what is false or implausible from what is true. Grand conspiracy theories can be useful tools, as long as you use them as a benchmark for bad logic—instead of blindly following them—and use their example to improve your own thinking.

Closing

The Internet has been a great advancement for society. People now have more easily accessible information in the palm of their hand than they could have dreamed about a generation ago. However, not all of this information is reliable. Some of it, like the idea that a "suburban mom" has found the cure to a problem that's bedeviled dermatologists for decades, or that someone in a remote village found an herb that cures breast cancer, is extraordinary to the point of being literally unbelievable. So how are people supposed to find information that is reliable, or even true?

Critical thinking is useful, but one needs reliable and true information to base it upon.

Otherwise, how will people be able to reach true conclusions? Here are some procedures you can follow to use critical thinking well in everyday life.

The first thing to do is verify the information found in online sources. The best way to do this is to check multiple outlets that are independent, run by people who know what they are talking about, and fact-checked if possible. Always search for multiple sources and see if they reach a consensus. This is not always easy on the Internet; many different websites rely on one core article, for example, and just repeat it over and over. One way to counteract this is to look for websites that take the opposite position and see if they are reliable. The only way to judge what is correct is to have a good idea of the entire landscape of the issue. Often, one side of the issue is much more reliable than the other, which makes the more trustworthy side a good bet.

The biggest component of reliability, of course, is the quality of the website. A key giveaway for this is whether it looks old, or like if it is professionally managed. Websites with a strong political message, emotional tone, or that look like they are trying to sell a product are generally not reliable. Websites about controversial topics, such as a radically political website for example, also tend to be very biased. For controversial topics, it is especially important to find a variety of sources with different views to find reliable information. Some topics that are controversial even among experts, like human-caused climate change, merit the most careful consideration of all. Most scientists agree that human-based climate change is real, but some scientists still deny its existence. In this case, it is important to research the scientists themselves to see if they are paid by oil companies or political parties, to better account for their biases and assess their scientific opinions.

Critical thinking cannot replace knowledge. Rather, the two go hand-in-hand. It is important to research the topics one wants to investigate before practicing critical thinking and forming an opinion. However, critical thinking is important to assessing this researched information, and seeing what would make a true premise and what would not. If one relies solely on accumulated knowledge without using critical thinking skills, it is easy to fall into logical traps or biases like the ones described in this book. Therefore, in today's information-heavy world, it is important to keep the balance between the two in mind, and use them both to form better, more truth-oriented opinions.

A.R.

Reference

AP Psychology Community. Neisser and Harsch.
AP Psychology Community. 2018.
https://www.appsychology.com/IB%20Psych/IBc
ontent/Studies/Neisser%20and%20Harsch.htm

Bradford, Alina. Deductive reasoning vs.
Inductive reasoning. Live Science. 2017.
https://www.livescience.com/21569-deduction-vs-
induction.html

Burton, Neel. Our Hierarchy of Needs.
Psychology Today. 2012.
https://www.psychologytoday.com/us/blog/hide-
and-seek/201205/our-hierarchy-needs

Cahn, Lauren. 12 crazy conspiracy theories that
actually turned out to be true. Readers Digest.
2019. http://www.readersdigest.com.au/true-
stories-lifestyle/12-crazy-conspiracy-theories-
actually-turned-out-be-true

Cheriyedath, Susha. What is a Phantom Limb?
News Medical. 2019. https://www.news-
medical.net/health/What-is-a-Phantom-Limb.aspx

Critical Thinking Web. What is Critical Thinking? Philosophy. 2019.
https://philosophy.hku.hk/think/critical/ct.php

Gundacker, Felix. Genealogical Dictionary (PDF). Archived from the original (PDF) on 2014-04-19. 2013.

Hasher, Lynn; Goldstein, David; Toppino, Thomas. Frequency and the conference of referential validity. Journal of Verbal Learning and Verbal Behavior. 16 (1): 107–112. doi:10.1016/S0022-5371(77)80012-1. 1977.

Higgins, Chris. The McGurk Effect. Mental Floss. 2015.
http://mentalfloss.com/article/72587/mcgurk-effect-or-brains-are-weird

Hyslop, J. H. The Elements of Logic, Theoretical and Practical. C. Scribner's Sons. 1892. 2019.https://www.logicallyfallacious.com/tools/lp/Bo/LogicalFallacies/136/Non-Sequitur

Issues In Forensic Psychology. 2019.
https://sites.google.com/site/consultingservicesinfo/criminal-justice-issues/false-memory-contamination

Jackson, John. The Ideomotor Effect. Critical Thinking. 2005. http://www.critical-thinking.org.uk/psychology/the-ideomotor-effect.php

Kahane, Howard. Logic and Contemporary Rhetoric: The Use of Reason in Everyday Life, 8th edition. 1997.

Komninos, Andreas. Our Three Brains - The Reptilian Brain. Interaction Design. 2018. https://www.interaction-design.org/literature/article/our-three-brains-the-reptilian-brain

Lopez, Kenji. The Burger Lab. he Burger Lab: Revisiting the Myth of The 12-Year Old McDonald's Burger That Just Won't Rot (Testing Results!) Serious Eats. 2010. https://aht.seriouseats.com/2010/11/the-burger-lab-revisiting-the-myth-of-the-12-year-old-burger-testing-results.html

Madigan, Jamie. The Left Digit Effect. Psychology Today. 2013. https://www.psychologytoday.com/intl/blog/mind-games/201306/the-left-digit-effect-why-game-prices-end-in-99

Markman, Art. The Consistency of Flashbulb Memories. Psychology Today. 2015. https://www.psychologytoday.com/us/blog/ulterior-motives/201506/the-consistency-flashbulb-memorie

Mastin, Luke. Long Term Memory. The Human Memory. 2018. http://www.human-memory.net/types_long.html

Mastin, Luke. Short Term Memory. The Human Memory. 2018. http://www.human-memory.net/types_short.html

McLeod, Saul. Attention Models. Simply Psychology. 2018. https://www.simplypsychology.org/attention-models.html

Perras, Cindy. Metacognitive Strategies or "Thinking About My Thinking". Ldat School. 2019. https://www.ldatschool.ca/metacognitive-strategies-or-thinking-about-my-thinking/

Psycheducation. "3-Brains-In-One" Brain. Psycheducation. 2019. https://psycheducation.org/brain-tours/3-brains-in-one-brain/

Robinson, Eric. Extra Sensory Perception. The British Psychological Society. 2009. https://thepsychologist.bps.org.uk/volume-22/edition-7/extra-sensory-perception-controversial-debate

Schacter, D.L., Harbluk, J.L., and McLachlen, D.R. Retrieval without recollection: an experimental analysis of source amnesia. Journal of Verbal Learning and Verbal Behaviour. 23 (5): 593–611. doi:10.1016/S0022-5371(84)90373-6. 1984.

Skeptical Raptor. Godwin's Law. Skeptical Raptor. 2019.
https://www.skepticalraptor.com/skepticalraptorbl og.php/logical-fallacies/godwins-law/

Skeptical Raptor. Post Hoc Ergo Propter Hoc. Skeptical Raptor. 2019.
https://www.skepticalraptor.com/skepticalraptorbl og.php/logical-fallacies/post-hoc-ergo-propter-hoc-logical-fallies/

Smith, Kerry. Brain makes decisions before you even know it. Nature. 2008.
https://www.nature.com/news/2008/080411/full/n ews.2008.751.html

Sook, Alastair. The Strange Photographs Used. BBC. 2017.
http://www.bbc.com/culture/story/20170216-five-photographs-used-to-prove-conspiracy-theories

Sophie Sowden, Caroline Catmur, The Role of the Right Temporoparietal Junction in the Control of Imitation, Cerebral Cortex, Volume 25, Issue 4, April 2015, Pages 1107–1113,
https://doi.org/10.1093/cercor/bht306.
Downloaded in 2019.

Terry Libkuman, Charles Stabler & Hajime Otani (2004) Arousal, valence, and memory for detail, Memory, 12:2, 237-247, DOI: 10.1080/09658210244000630

Todman, D. History of Neuroscience: Roger Sperry (1913-1994), IBRO History of Neuroscience. 2008. http://www.ibro1.info/Pub/Pub_Main_Display.asp?LC_Docs_ID=3473

Waterfield, Robin. Hidden Depths: The Story of Hypnosis. Pan Macmillan. ISBN: 9781447206903. 2011.

Weinshenk, Susan. Dopamine Seeking Reward Loop. Psychology Today. 2018. https://www.psychologytoday.com/intl/blog/brain-wise/201802/the-dopamine-seeking-reward-loop

Wiseman, Richard. Total Recall. Quirkology. 2019. http://www.richardwiseman.com/quirkology/new/USA/Experiment_totalRecall.shtml

Endnotes

[i] Critical Thinking Web. What is Critical Thinking? Philosophy. 2019.
https://philosophy.hku.hk/think/critical/ct.php

[ii] Perras, Cindy. Metacognitive Strategies or "Thinking About My Thinking". Ldat School. 2019.
https://www.ldatschool.ca/metacognitive-strategies-or-thinking-about-my-thinking/

[iii] Psycheducation. "3-Brains-In-One" Brain. Psycheducation. 2019.
https://psycheducation.org/brain-tours/3-brains-in-one-brain/

[iv] Komninos, Andreas. Our Three Brains - The Reptilian Brain. Interaction Design. 2018.
https://www.interaction-design.org/literature/article/our-three-brains-the-reptilian-brain

[v] Burton, Neel. Our Hierarchy of Needs. Psychology Today. 2012.
https://www.psychologytoday.com/us/blog/hide-and-seek/201205/our-hierarchy-needs

[vi] Weinshenk, Susan. Dopamine Seeking Reward Loop. Psychology Today. 2018.

https://www.psychologytoday.com/intl/blog/brai
n-wise/201802/the-dopamine-seeking-reward-
loop

[vii] Higgins, Chris. The McGurk Effect. Mental Floss.
2015.
http://mentalfloss.com/article/72587/mcgurk-
effect-or-brains-are-weird)

[viii] Mastin, Luke. Short Term Memory. The Human
Memory. 2018. http://www.human-
memory.net/types_short.html

[ix] Mastin, Luke. Long Term Memory. The Human
Memory. 2018. http://www.human-
memory.net/types_long.html

[x] Wiseman, Richard. Total Recall. Quirkology.
2019.
http://www.richardwiseman.com/quirkology/ne
w/USA/Experiment_totalRecall.shtml

[xi] Markman, Art. The Consistency of Flashbulb
Memories. Psychology Today. 2015.
https://www.psychologytoday.com/us/blog/ulteri
or-motives/201506/the-consistency-flashbulb-
memories

[xii]AP Psychology Community. Neisser and Harsch.
AP Psychology Community. 2018.
https://www.appsychology.com/IB%20Psych/IBc
ontent/Studies/Neisser%20and%20Harsch.htm

[xiii] Schacter, D.L., Harbluk, J.L., and McLachlen,
D.R. Retrieval without recollection: an
experimental analysis of source amnesia. Journal

of Verbal Learning and Verbal Behaviour. 23 (5): 593–611. doi:10.1016/S0022-5371(84)90373-6. 1984.

[xiv] Waterfield, Robin. Hidden Depths: The Story of Hypnosis. Pan Macmillan. ISBN: 9781447206903. 2011.

[xv] Hasher, Lynn; Goldstein, David; Toppino, Thomas. Frequency and the conference of referential validity. Journal of Verbal Learning and Verbal Behavior. 16 (1): 107–112. doi:10.1016/S0022-5371(77)80012-1. 1977.

[xvi] Terry Libkuman, Charles Stabler & Hajime Otani (2004) Arousal, valence, and memory for detail, Memory, 12:2, 237-247, DOI: 10.1080/09658210244000630

[xvii] McLeod, Saul. Attention Models. Simply Psychology. 2018. https://www.simplypsychology.org/attention-models.html

[xviii] Issues In Forensic Psychology. 2019. https://sites.google.com/site/consultingservicesinfo/criminal-justice-issues/false-memory-contamination

[xix] Smith, Kerry. Brain makes decisions before you even know it. Nature. 2008. https://www.nature.com/news/2008/080411/full/news.2008.751.html

[xx] Sophie Sowden, Caroline Catmur, The Role of the Right Temporoparietal Junction in the Control

of Imitation, Cerebral Cortex, Volume 25, Issue 4, April 2015, Pages 1107–1113, https://doi.org/10.1093/cercor/bht306. Downloaded in 2019.

[xxi] Todman, D. History of Neuroscience: Roger Sperry (1913-1994), IBRO History of Neuroscience. 2008. http://www.ibro1.info/Pub/Pub_Main_Display.asp?LC_Docs_ID=3473

[xxii] Cheriyedath, Susha. What is a Phantom Limb? News Medical. 2019. https://www.news-medical.net/health/What-is-a-Phantom-Limb.aspx

[xxiii] Jackson, John. The Ideomotor Effect. Critical Thinking. 2005. http://www.critical-thinking.org.uk/psychology/the-ideomotor-effect.php

[xxiv] Bradford, Alina. Deductive reasoning vs. Inductive reasoning. Live Science. 2017. https://www.livescience.com/21569-deduction-vs-induction.html

[xxv] Hyslop, J. H. The Elements of Logic, Theoretical and Practical. C. Scribner's Sons. 1892. 2019.https://www.logicallyfallacious.com/tools/lp/Bo/LogicalFallacies/136/Non-Sequitur

[xxvi] Kahane, Howard. Logic and Contemporary Rhetoric: The Use of Reason in Everyday Life, 8th edition. 1997.

xxvii Skeptical Raptor. Post Hoc Ergo Propter Hoc.
Skeptical Raptor. 2019.
https://www.skepticalraptor.com/skepticalraptor
blog.php/logical-fallacies/post-hoc-ergo-propter-
hoc-logical-fallies/
xxviii Robinson, Eric. Extra Sensory Perception. The
British Psychological Society. 2009.
https://thepsychologist.bps.org.uk/volume-
22/edition-7/extra-sensory-perception-
controversial-debate
xxix Sook, Alastair. The Strange Photographs Used.
BBC. 2017.
http://www.bbc.com/culture/story/20170216-
five-photographs-used-to-prove-conspiracy-
theories
xxx Skeptical Raptor. Godwin's Law. Skeptical
Raptor. 2019.
https://www.skepticalraptor.com/skepticalraptor
blog.php/logical-fallacies/godwins-law/
xxxi Lopez, Kenj. The Burger Lab. he Burger Lab:
Revisiting the Myth of The 12-Year Old
McDonald's Burger That Just Won't Rot (Testing
Results!) Serious Eats. 2010.
https://aht.seriouseats.com/2010/11/the-burger-
lab-revisiting-the-myth-of-the-12-year-old-
burger-testing-results.html
xxxii Madigan, Jamie. The Left Digit Effect.
Psychology Today. 2013.
https://www.psychologytoday.com/intl/blog/min

d-games/201306/the-left-digit-effect-why-game-prices-end-in-99

[xxxiii] Gundacker, Felix. Genealogical Dictionary (PDF). Archived from the original (PDF) on 2014-04-19. 2013.

[xxxiv] Cahn, Lauren. 12 crazy conspiracy theories that actually turned out to be true. Readers Digest. 2019.

http://www.readersdigest.com.au/true-stories-lifestyle/12-crazy-conspiracy-theories-actually-turned-out-be-true